The Sower and his Seed

Early one morning a  filled his  with and went into his field to sow them.

Some fell on the road and the  flew down from the  and ate them.

Some landed in a thorn

and the long sharp thorns choked the

tiny  and they died.

But the  went on sowing his

 until his was empty,

and all the rest of his fell on

ground that was good.

These tiny grew and grew into

a field of lovely golden corn.

The Lost Sheep

A  cares for every one of his

 . There was once a good

who was ready to fight a

or a  for his  .

One night this good counted

his as usual only to find there

was one missing. One of his

was lost.

The were bright in the night

sky as the  began his search

for the lost  . He heard a

 howl and he was afraid. After

a long search he found his lost

and carried it home.

The  didn't mind being so

tired. He was just happy that his lost

 was safe.

The Good Samaritan

One day a weary  was riding

along a lonely road when suddenly,

fierce sprang at him from the

 .

The dragged him from his

 and took everything he had,

even some of his  .

The lay half-dead at the road side with the hot beating down on him.

Soon along that narrow road people

came – a 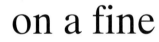 on a fine  ,

another on a  . Both men

looked the other way when they saw

the poor wounded and

hurried on.

Then round the bend came another

man on a  . This was the  .

He stopped and went to help the

dying  . He gave him water to

drink and bound up his wounds

before lifting him on to his

and taking him to the nearest

"Take care of this poor ," said the  to the . "Here are some silver . If you spend more I will repay you on my return ...!"

"I will indeed," said the , wishing that all men had kind hearts like the .

The King and the Cruel Servant

There was once a powerful  who lived in a fine  . One day the discovered that his trusted  had cheated him out of a huge amount of .

"You must pay back what you owe!" cried the angry  , "or go to

prison."

"I cannot!" wailed the ,

falling on his knees. "I have a

and two ..."

The was moved to pity as the  begged for forgiveness. "I forgive you," he said at last. "And you need not pay back the ."

In high spirits the  left the  But at the  who should he meet but the young  !

The  was leading a  .

"Stop!" shouted the  . "You owe me money!"

"I cannot pay you," said the
tearfully. "Forgive me! I have an old
 to look after ..."

"I won't forgive you!" cried the cruel
 . "Never!"

And he told the  to put the
 in prison.

The next day the  sent for the

cruel  .

"I showed you mercy," he said in a

stern voice. "I forgave you. But you,

in your turn, did not forgive that

poor  ." And the

ordered his  to throw the cruel

 into one of the deepest